Usborne English Readers

Level 2

THE WOODEN HORSE

Retold by Mairi Mackinnon

Illustrated by Alida Massari

English language consultant: Peter Viney

Contents

You can listen to the story online here:
www.usborneenglishreaders.com/
woodenhorse

The sun was shining brightly on the island of Ithaca. The King and his young Queen were sitting under the fruit trees outside the palace. Their small son was playing on the ground beside them.

"I must be the happiest man in the world," said King Odysseus. "I live on the most beautiful island. I have the most beautiful wife…"

"The second most beautiful," said his queen, smiling.

"Are you thinking of Helen?" said Odysseus. "She's just trouble. You are so much better than her, my love."

The Queen put her hand on his shoulder. "Oh, I'm not jealous of Helen, not at all. I don't think her beauty makes her happy...

Husband, dear, look there on the sea. Isn't that a ship?"

A little later, when the soldiers came up the hill to the palace, Odysseus recognized them. "You've come from King Menelaus, haven't you?" he said. "What is it, good news or bad?"

"It's very bad," they said. "The King needs your help. Queen Helen is missing."
"Missing? What do you mean?"

"She's just… gone. We had some visitors from the city of Troy.

Their Prince Paris couldn't stop looking at Helen.

When the Trojans left, Helen was with them. Menelaus is really angry. He wants to kill Paris."

"I can believe that," said Odysseus. "I'm sorry to hear it, but what do you want me to do?"

"Menelaus wants to take an army to Troy,
and bring Helen back. He is asking all the
kings in Greece to help him. You're his
closest friend, Odysseus. Come with us."

"Menelaus has so many friends," said
Odysseus. "Some of them don't have wives
and families. Why don't you ask them?"

"You're also the cleverest man
in Greece. Please, Odysseus. You
can come back to Ithaca as soon as
Menelaus has Helen again. It won't
take long. You'll see – the Trojans
won't want a war."

The messengers were wrong. Hundreds of ships sailed from Greece to Troy. They brought thousands of brave fighting men – but Troy had an army too, and high walls and strong gates. Again and again the Greeks attacked the city, but the Trojans stayed safe inside the city walls. The war lasted for ten long years.

"We can't go on," Odysseus told Menelaus.
"We've lost too many good soldiers. The men
are exhausted, and they want to go home.
I want to go home.

I miss Ithaca. I miss my wife and my boy.
I haven't seen him since he was a baby."

"We're not leaving until we have Helen,"
Menelaus insisted. "You're the clever one,
Odysseus. Can't you think of something?"

Odysseus was awake and thinking all night. In the morning, he had a plan.

"We can't just attack the city again," he said. "The walls are too high and the gates are too strong for us. We need to open the gates from the inside."

"How can we do that?" Menelaus asked.

"With a trick," answered Odysseus.

"A clever trick."

A short way from the army camp, there was a forest. Odysseus took some of the soldiers there. All day they cut the tall trees, and shaped the wood. Then they started building something.

At first it looked like a huge farmer's cart, on four wooden wheels.

But the men were still building,
higher and higher: four huge legs,
an enormous body, a head…
"A *horse*?" asked Menelaus.
"A wooden horse," said Odysseus.
"Big enough for me to hide inside,
with some of your best soldiers."

That evening, Menelaus's army got ready to leave. Very early the next morning, the men loaded their boats. Then they burned the rest of the camp.

They sailed away, but they didn't sail very far.

Near Troy, there was a long, low island. As soon as the ships were on the other side of it, the soldiers made a new camp. They couldn't see the city, so that meant the Trojans couldn't see them. The men rested there, and waited.

A little later, the Trojan guards looked out from the city walls.

"What's happening? The Greeks have gone!"

"Their camp is burning!"

"And what's *that*, in front of the gates?"

"Wait, there's a man beside it – a Greek soldier. He's holding up his hands…"

The guards brought the man inside the
gates. Everyone in the city came to watch.

"Please don't kill me," the soldier begged.
"My name is Sinon. I am Greek, but I hate
the Greeks. I'm glad they've gone. I hate the
war, so I ran away from the army. They were
going to kill me. I don't want to die."

"But why did they leave so suddenly?"

"They can't win," said Sinon, "and they know it. The gods must be angry with them. For ten years the Greeks tried to get into the city, but they couldn't. Finally they have understood – if the gods won't help them, what can they do?"

"And what's that *thing*, that horse?"

"They made it as a present for the gods, so that they can sail home safely – they hope. *I* hope they all die."

"It's a sign," the people said. "We should bring the horse into the city, and take it to the temple. The gods will be pleased."

"Don't do it!" said the Trojan princess Cassandra. "Something terrible will happen!" But nobody listened to her – they never did. The Trojans opened the huge city gates, and brought the horse inside.

Everyone in Troy was glad that the war was over, from the oldest to the youngest. They filled their temple with flowers, and laughed and danced in the streets. There was food and drink and music everywhere.

Finally, they went to their homes to sleep. They were exhausted after ten years of war. Even the guards at the city gates were sleeping.

In the middle of the night, Sinon saw
lights out at sea. It was a sign that the
Greek ships were coming back. The Greek
army would soon be ready outside the gates.

Sinon went to the wooden horse and opened a secret door in its body.

Odysseus climbed out first. "Well done, my friend," he said. Thirty-nine soldiers followed him. They had swords in their hands, ready to fight. Very quietly, they went to the gates and opened them.

Suddenly there was noise everywhere as the Greek army rushed into the city. The streets filled with the sounds of shouting and screaming. The Trojans tried to find their swords, but they were half asleep and they weren't even ready to fight.

Soon houses were burning, dogs were barking and frightened children were crying.

Nothing could stop the Greek soldiers. They fought all the way through the city, from the walls to the King's palace and the temple. "Where is Helen?" roared Menelaus.

At last they found her, hiding in the temple. "Please, take me home," she said. "The Trojans hate me. Only Paris and his brother were kind to me, and now they are dead. This war is all my fault, but I never wanted it. Oh, Menelaus, I have been so unhappy."

Menelaus looked at his wife, and he couldn't be angry with her. "You haven't changed, Helen," he said quietly. "You're as beautiful as ever. Come with me. It's time for us all to go home."

The next day, the Greeks left the
ruined city. They were shouting and
laughing, glad that the fighting was over.
They were alive, and they were going
home at last.

Before they sailed away, they loaded
their ships with Trojan treasure.

Menelaus put his arm around Helen. "This is my treasure," he said. "And you, Odysseus, soon you'll see your wife again, and your son too."

Odysseus was exhausted, but he smiled at his friend. "Yes," he said. "I hope I will."

About the story

Thousands of years ago, in Greece, people told lots of stories about the Greek gods and kings and queens. The story of the wooden horse was probably one of them. There were no books of stories at the time. Instead, storytellers listened to the stories, then remembered them and told other people.

Over 2,500 years ago, the Greek poet Homer mentioned the story of the wooden horse in *The Odyssey*. The rest of *The Odyssey* is about Odysseus's long, dangerous journey home from Troy. It was ten years before he saw his wife and son again in Ithaca.

Here you can see part of a pot from the island of Mykonos in Greece. It's as old as Homer's poem. It shows the wooden horse and the soldiers hiding inside.

Activities

The answers are on page 40.

Who's who?

Choose two sentences for each person.

 Odysseus
 Helen
 Menelaus
 Paris

A.
He's the
Prince of
Troy.

B.
He lives on
the island of
Ithaca.

C.
She's married
to King
Menelaus.

D.
He asks
Odysseus for
help.

E.
He finds
Helen hiding
in the temple.

F.
He's the
cleverest man
in Greece.

G.
King Menelaus
wants to
kill him.

H.
She's the most
beautiful woman
in Greece.

Mixed-up story

Can you put these pictures and sentences in order?

A.

The Greek army rushed into the city.

B.

Everyone in Troy was glad that the war was over.

C.

The soldiers built an enormous wooden horse.

D.

Hundreds of ships sailed from Greece to Troy..

E.

Odysseus thought of a plan.

F.

The Greeks loaded their boats with treasure.

G.

The Trojans brought the horse into the city.

H.

Some messengers visited King Odysseus.

I.

Odysseus climbed out first.

Where are they?

Choose one word from the list to finish each sentence.

1.

The King and Queen sat
.... the fruit trees.

2.

"There's a man........... it,"
said the guard.

under

outside

3.

The Trojans brought Sinon
.... the gate.

4.

They rested on an island
.... Troy.

beside

around

5.

The Greek army would
soon be ready ....
the gates.

6.

Meneleus put his arm
.... Helen.

near

inside

What are they saying?

Choose the right word to finish each sentence.

1.

I must be the .... man in the world.

handsomest
cleverest
happiest

2.

I'm ....to hear that Helen is missing.

angry
sorry
happy

3.

We can't go on. The men are ....

enormous
exhausted
gone

4.

I've thought of a .... trick.

safe
small
clever

Which is true?

Choose the right sentence for each picture.

1.

A. Cassandra told the Trojans that something terrible would happen.

B. Cassandra told the Trojans to bring the horse into the city.

2.

A. King Menelaus stopped looking at Helen.

B. Paris couldn't stop looking at Helen.

3.

A. All day, the soldiers cut and shaped the tall trees.

B. All day, the soldiers rested under the tall trees.

4.

A. Sinon said that the Greeks wanted to kill him.

B. Sinon said that the horse was full of Greek soldiers.

Word list

army (n) hundreds or thousands of soldiers fighting together for a city or a country.

bark (v) when a dog barks, it makes a loud noise to show that it is excited or angry.

beg (v) to ask for something that you want very badly.

camp (n) a place where people stay for a short time, usually in tents.

cart (n) something with wheels for moving or carrying heavy things. Long ago, before there were cars or trucks, horses pulled carts.

exhausted (adj) very, very tired.

glad (adj) happy about something.

gods (n) long ago in Greece, people believed in different gods. When the gods were pleased, good things happened to people.

guard (n) a soldier who protects a person or a place.

huge (adj) very big.

insist (v) when you insist, you say that something *must* happen.

last (v) to take time; for example, "the lesson lasts an hour".

load (v) to put something into a boat (or a cart or a truck) to carry it.

messenger (n) a person who brings
a message is a messenger.

(my) fault (n) if something bad happens because of
you, or because of something you did, it is your fault.

roar (v) when wild animals or people roar, they make a loud
noise to show that they are angry or they want to fight.

ruined (adj) when buildings are ruined,
they are broken and spoiled.

rush (v) to go somewhere very quickly.

sail (v) when a boat travels from one
place to another, it sails.

shape (v) to make something into a shape.

sign (n) a sign tells you something,
or tells you to do something.

temple (n) a building where people worship gods.

treasure (n) precious and valuable
things, like gold and silver.

Trojan (n, adj) from the city of Troy.

visitor (n) someone who comes from another
place and stays for a short time is a visitor.

war (n) when armies fight for a long time.

wooden (adj) made of wood.

Answers

Who's who?
Odysseus – B, F
Helen – C, H
Menelaus – D, E
Paris – A, G

Mixed-up story
H, D, E, C, G,
B, I, A, F

Where are they?
1. under   2. beside
3. inside   4. near
5. outside 6. around

What are they saying?
1. happiest
2. sorry
3. exhausted
4. clever

Which is true?
1. A
2. B
3. A
4. A

You can find information about other
Usborne English Readers here:
www.usborneenglishreaders.com

Designed by Sam Whibley and Hope Reynolds
Series designer: Laura Nelson Norris
Edited by Jane Chisholm
With thanks to Rosie Hore
Digital imaging by Nick Wakeford

Page 32: photo by Leemage/UIG © Getty Images

First published in 2016 by Usborne Publishing Ltd.,
Usborne House, 83-85 Saffron Hill, London EC1N 8RT, England.
www.usborne.com Copyright © 2016 Usborne Publishing Ltd.

All rights reserved. No part of this publication may be reproduced, stored in a retrieval system or transmitted in any
form or by any means, electronic, mechanical, photocopying, recording or otherwise, without the prior permission of
the publisher. The name Usborne and the devices ♀⊕ are Trade Marks of Usborne Publishing Ltd. UE.